Summer Solutions.

Minutes a Day–Mastery for a Lifetime!

Standards-Based
ENGLISH GRAMMAR
& Mechanics

4

Nancy L. McGraw   Joan Archer
Nancy Tondy   Diane Dillon
Regina Webb   Patricia Kecskemety

Simple Solutions Learning, Inc.
Beachwood, OH

Summer Solutions
Standards-Based
English Grammar & Mechanics 4

The writers of *Summer Solutions* Standards-Based English Grammar & Mechanics aligned the series in accordance with information from the following:

National Governors Association Center for Best Practices, Council of Chief State School Officers, Washington, D.C., 2010.

Printed in the United States of America

ISBN: 978-1-60873-521-1

Cover Design: Dan Mazzola
Editor: Rebecca Toukonen

Instructions for Parents / Guardians

- *Summer Solutions* is an extension of the *Simple Solutions* Approach being used by thousands of children in schools across the United States.

- This summer book aligns with English Language Arts standards that identify key ideas, understandings, and skills appropriate for this particular grade level. The standards' codes are listed next to the reviewed skills.

- The 30 lessons included in each workbook are meant to review and reinforce the skills learned in the grade level just completed.

- The program is designed to be used three days per week for ten weeks to ensure retention. Completing the book all at one time defeats the purpose of sustained practice over the summer break.

- The answers for each lesson are found in the back of the book. Lessons should be checked immediately after completion for optimal feedback. Items that were difficult for students or done incorrectly should be resolved right away to ensure mastery.

- Adjust the use of the book to fit vacations. More lessons may have to be completed during the weeks before or following a family vacation.

Summer Solutions
Standards-Based
English Grammar & Mechanics 4

Reviewed Skills Include   Standard

- Use relative pronouns and relative adverbs..L.4.1a
- Form and use the progressive verb tenses...L.4.1b
- Form and use prepositional phrases L.4.1e
- Produce complete sentences, recognizing and correcting inappropriate fragments and run-ons*..L.4.1f
- Correctly use frequently confused words..L.4.1g
- Use correct capitalization..L.4.2a
- Use commas and quotation marks to mark direct speech and quotations from a text..L.4.2b
- Use a comma before a coordinating conjunction in a compound sentence..L.4.2c
- Use knowledge of language and its conventions when writing, speaking, reading, or listening L.4.3
- Use context as a clue to the meaning of a word or phrase............L.4.4a
- Use common, grade-appropriate Greek and Latin affixes and roots..L.4.4b
- Explain the meaning of simple similes and metaphors in context...L.4.5a
- Recognize and explain the meaning of common idioms, adages, and proverbs L.4.5b
- Describe the overall structure of events, ideas, concepts, or information in a text RI.4.5

Help Pages begin on page 63.
Answers to Lessons begin on page 73.

Lesson #1

1. **A noun names a person, place, or thing. To make most nouns plural, add -*s*.** Add (s) to make the noun plural.

   Mom left three <u>Messages</u> for you. (message)

2. **The relative pronouns are *who, whom, whose, which*, and *that*. Relative pronouns are related, or connected, to an antecedent. *Who*, *whom*, and *whose* are used with people.** Choose the correct relative pronoun.

   Bill and Brent are the ones <u>who</u> know all the baseball trivia.

   which   whom   (who)

3. Add commas in a series.

   Polly bought ice-cream, nuts, candy, and cookies for the party.

4. Underline the two things being compared in this simile.

   <u>The sky last night</u> was as clear as a <u>bell</u>.

5. Choose the best meaning for the underlined word.

   Jenna is such a <u>magpie</u>! She <u>never stops</u> talking!

   (talkative person)   tasty dessert   reading material

6. *It's* is a contraction meaning "it is." *Its* is a possessive pronoun.

   Choose the correct word.

   (It's / Its) too cold for swimming.

   Watch the bird build (its / it's) nest.

7. **A sentence is a group of words that expresses a complete thought. A sentence must include a subject and a verb.** Circle the subject and underline the verb in the following sentence.

   Claire swims in the pool at Quarry Park.

8. Find the word *persistent* in a thesaurus. Choose two synonyms for *persistent*.

   continuous   determined   hesitant   quitting

9. **The progressive tense is formed with a main verb that ends in *-ing* and a helping verb to show action that is ongoing. The action can be in the past, present or future.**

   Complete the sentence to show *ongoing action in the present.*

   Kara is frosting the cupcakes for the party.

   will be frosting   frosted   is frosting

10. Choose the synonym for the underlined word.

    We saw a <u>huge</u> alligator in the swamp.

    scary   angry   scaly   enormous

Lesson #2

1. **A proper noun names a particular person, place, or thing. Always begin a proper noun with a capital letter.** Underline the proper nouns.

   <u>Reggie</u>   plane   <u>China</u>   <u>Boston</u>   marshmallow

2. **A pronoun renames an antecedent. The antecedent and the pronoun must agree.**

   Example: We groomed the *horses* after we rode *them*.

            plural **antecedent**   plural **pronoun**

   Choose the pronoun that agrees with the underlined noun.

   Macy tried on tennis <u>shoes</u> and bought (it / (them)).

   Chance baked a <u>cake</u> and brought ((it) / them) to the picnic.

3. ***Can* is a special helping verb that is used in place of "able to" or "permission to."** Match each sentence with the way *can* is used.

   A) Mark <u>can</u> play golf very well.   __A__ is able to

   B) He <u>can</u> practice at the range anytime he wants.   __B__ has permission to

4. Use the proofreader's symbol for "make capital" to show which words should be capitalized in this sentence. (See *Help Pages*.)

   <u>l</u>iza and <u>m</u>arcus live on <u>b</u>rower <u>r</u>oad.

5. **Quotation marks are a frame around spoken words.** Add quotation marks to the sentence.

   "Would you like to go camping with us?" Asher asked.

6. **A sentence that combines two complete thoughts with a coordinating conjunction is a compound sentence.** (See *Help Pages* for a list of coordinating conjunctions.) Underline the two complete thoughts in this sentence.

It is raining, so <u>our baseball game will be cancelled</u>.

7. Remember, add *-es* to make a word plural if it ends in *s, x, z, ch*, or *sh*. Write the plurals.

peach _peaches_   mix _Mixes_   kiss _kisses_

8. Use the prefix *im-* to write a word that means "not polite."

impolite

9 – 10. Write a short note to your friend. Tell about your summer. Use informal English.

Dear _Bob_____,

My summer is going awsome, and I basically go to camp every week. some camps are fun, but some camps aren't fun.

Lesson #3

1. **A concrete noun is something you can see, touch, taste, hear, and smell. An abstract noun names something you cannot see or touch.** Underline the concrete noun(s) and circle the abstract noun in each sentence.

   The principal will discover the truth.

   I do not have a fear of spiders or snakes.

2. Read the sentence. Underline the part that states a cause.

   When George put his ivy plant near a sunny window, it began to grow long leafy vines.

3. **A preposition shows how words in a sentence are related. A noun or a pronoun comes after a preposition.** Use the *Help Pages* to write five prepositions below.

   by, into, up, out, of

4. Match each idiom with its meaning.

   close but no cigar   at the last minute

   at the eleventh hour   correct answer or idea

   that's the ticket   not quite

5. **Adjectives describe nouns in many different ways. Adjectives tell *what kind* and *how many*.** Circle the adjectives that describe the underlined nouns.

   A large fierce dog barked furiously at the unknown intruder.

6. Show that proper nouns begin with a capital letter. Use the proofreader's symbol (≡) under each proper noun.

Monday, mrs. sands took kay and the boys to ginger island.

7. Insert commas where they belong.

We are selling candy bars, popcorn, pretzels, and gum.

Please bring your swimsuit, towel, sunscreen, and a snack to the pool party.

8. Underline all the adjectives.

March was a cold, snowy month but July should be a hot, sunny one.

9. Choose the correct past tense verb.

Isabel had accidentally (throw / threw / thrown) the paper in the trash.

10. Use a verb of being in a sentence. (*is, am, are, was, were, be, being, been*)

I am very mad

Lesson #4

1. **Remember, adverbs tell *how, when,* or *where* the action of a verb takes place.** Which word in this sentence is an adverb? Underline the adverb. Draw an arrow to the verb it describes.

   I will gladly ~~go~~ with you to the holiday parade.

2. Insert commas in a series.

   Jamal has birds, cats, dogs, turtles, and hamsters as pets.

3. **A coordinating conjunction can connect two complete thoughts in a sentence.** Place a comma before the conjunction.

   Paulette wants a new bike, but she hasn't saved enough money.

4. **Adjectives tell *size, shape, age,* and *color*.** Circle the adjectives that tell *color*. Underline adjectives that tell *size*.

   Victoria wore a long (purple) skirt and yellow blouse.

   Missy bought a small (red) purse.

5. Choose the correct relative pronoun.

   Mary, __who__ is in my class, lives next door to my aunt.

   whom   which   (who)

6. Write the <u>present progressive form</u> of the verb *come*.

Gerry ___*is goiang*___ to the movies.

7. **A sentence always begins with a capital letter and ends with a punctuation mark. It expresses a complete thought.**

Underline the sentence that is correct.

I'd love to hike in the park

the pool is closed!

<u>What is this movie about?</u>

8. What is the meaning of the underlined word in the sentence?

My teacher asked me why I looked so <u>blue</u>.

color   (sad or unhappy)   a bruise mark

9. **A title, such as aunt, Mr., or president, is capitalized when it is used before a person's name. Titles are usually not capitalized when used alone.**

Underline five words that should begin with a capital letter.

<u>i</u> went with <u>aunt mary</u> to hear <u>senator</u> <u>brown</u> speak.

10. When a word ends in a consonant plus *y*, usually change the *y* to *i* and add *es* to make the plural.

Change the *y* to *i* and add *es* to these words.

injury ___*injuries*___   baby ___*babies*___

Lesson #5

1. **The subject tells *whom* or *what* a sentence is about. A verb tells what the subject *is* or *does*.** Underline the subject in the sentence. Circle the verb.

   <u>Mr. Torrez</u> gave us some interesting books to read.

2. **Subject-Verb Agreement: When the subject is singular, add *-s* to the verb. When the subject is plural do not add *-s* to the verb.** Choose the present tense verb that will complete the sentence.

   Alex and Lisa (plays / (play)) baseball in the summer.

   Tory ((adds) / add) the numbers in the math problem.

3. The word *logical* means "reasonable." What is the meaning of *illogical*?   <u>not reasonable</u>

4. Choose the <u>past progressive form</u> of the verb.

   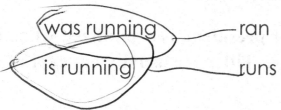

   (was running) —— ran

   (is running) —— runs

5. **A fragment is not a sentence because it does not express a complete thought.**

   What is missing from this <u>fragment</u>?

   five picnic baskets   (subject) / verb

   Correctly rewrite it as a complete sentence. Include proper capitalization and punctuation.

   <u>Suzie has five picnic baskets</u>

6. **Always capitalize the pronoun *I*.**

Underline the words that should be capitalized in each sentence.

<u>suki</u> and <u>i</u> are going swimming together.

<u>my</u> friend and <u>i</u> went to the playground.

7. Use the proofreader's symbols for "add something" and "make capital" to fix this sentence. (See *Help Pages* if needed.) Rewrite the sentence correctly.

dr. hanson is dentist.

Dr. Hanson is dentist.

8. Which two words are synonyms?

(quick)   impatient   friendly   (speedy)

9. Add the suffix *-ful* to make a word that means "full of help."

helpful

10. Underline the cause in this statement.

<u>There was a power failure,</u> so we had to light candles.

Lesson #6

1. **An action verb tells what the subject of a sentence *does*. Forms of the verb *be* (verbs of being) tell what the subject *is* or *was*.**

    Underline the verb in each sentence. Write B if it is a verb of being. Write A if it is an action verb.

    _____ My new bike is blue.

    _____ Meredith traveled to California.

    _____ Emily read her favorite book to the class.

    _____ Brian sings in the choir.

2. Write your own address with correct capitalization and punctuation.

    _____

3. Add the suffix *-less* to make a word that means "without use."

    _____

4. ***That* is a relative pronoun used to refer to things, but may refer to people.** Underline the relative pronoun. Draw an arrow to the antecedent.

    The team that wins gets to take home the trophy.

5. Circle the group of words that is a sentence.

         After the bell.   She lost her ring.   All the rest.

6. Insert the proofreader's symbols for "make lower case" and "add end punctuation" to fix this sentence. (See *Help Pages* if needed.)

We had Bagels and juice for breakfast

7. **When two complete thoughts are joined together in one sentence by a coordinating conjunction, a comma is needed before the conjunction.**

Add a comma before the coordinating conjunction in this compound sentence.

It is nine o'clock at night but it is still light outside.

8. Which words are antonyms?

narrow   quiet   wide   tall

9. What kind of sentence is this?

Wow, look at that!

A) declarative (statement)
B) exclamatory (exclamation)
C) imperative (command)
D) interrogative (question)

10. Underline the metaphor.

When it comes to work, Jason is a mule.

Lesson #7

1. **Verbs of being tell what the subject *is* or *was*. Verbs of being do not show action.** Write the eight verbs of being. (See *Help Pages*.)

    _____ _____ _____ _____

    _____ _____ _____ _____

2. **The verb tenses are *present*, *past*, and *future*. Present tense tells what is happening now. Past tense tells what has already happened. Future tense tells what will happen.**

    Write past, present, or future to tell the tense of these verbs.

    Marcy <u>planned</u> the party for her sister.   _____

    She <u>invites</u> Kassie's friends.   _____

    Tomorrow I <u>will ask</u> Mom to order the cake.   _____

3. Choose the <u>future progressive form</u> of the verb.

    will be walking   walks

    was walking   is walking

4. **Adjectives tell *size*, *shape*, *age*, and *color*.** Circle the adjectives that tell *shape*. Underline the adjectives that tell *age*.

    Jackie admired the old round table.

    Anthony chose a new rectangular desk.

5. Choose the correct word.

    I can't believe it took more than an
    (hour / our) to take (hour / our) achievement test.

6. **The name of a geographic location is a proper noun. It begins with a capital letter. The article *the* is not capitalized.**

    Underline the geographic locations that should be capitalized. Correctly rewrite the words on the line.

    My family likes to go sailing on lake erie near sandusky bay.

    _____

7. Use the proofreader's symbols for "add end punctuation" and "check spelling" to fix this sentence. (See *Help Pages* if needed.)

    It was the bigest snowstorm on record

    Write the sentence correctly.

    _____

8. What does the underlined part of the sentence tell?

    Leon won the scholarship because <u>he had the highest grades in the class</u>.

                    cause   effect

9. Choose two antonyms.

        expensive   filthy   cheap   dirty

10. Circle the meaning of the underlined word in the sentence.

    Jonathon rode 1,000 miles on his <u>stationary</u> bike and never left his basement.

        moving   still   speedy   motorcycle

Lesson #8

1. **Use the helping verb *have* when the subject is plural and use *has* when the subject is singular. Use *had* with singular or plural subjects.**

   Choose the correct helping verb.

   Emily (has / have) gone to the concert with Meredith.

   Krista and Kara (has / have) picked a basket of peaches.

2. Choose the correct word.

   (They're / Their / There) is a long road ahead.

3. Match each sentence with the way *can* is used.
   A) Mom says I can go to the movies.
   B) I can bake a cake by myself.

   _____ is able to

   _____ has permission to

4. Circle the preposition in each sentence. Use the *Help Pages* if needed.

   Cayla looked through the schedule.

   Lorna sat on the blanket.

5. Write the proofreader's symbol for "indent." _____

6. Choose the correct relative pronoun.

    The woman _____ drives the bus is very friendly.

    which   whom   who

7. **Always use a comma before a direct quote, and use quotation marks to frame the words that are spoken.**

    Insert the comma and quotation marks.

    Amanda asked May I borrow your camera?

8. What kind of sentence is this?

    Look for your shoes.

    A) declarative (statement)
    B) exclamatory (exclamation)
    C) imperative (command)
    D) interrogative (question)

9 – 10. **Remember a cause tells *what happened*; an effect tells *why*.** Make up a cause or effect and write them below.

    A) Cause: The thunderstorm had strong winds.

        Effect: _____

    B) Cause: _____

        Effect: All of the students were sent home early.

Lesson #9

1. Find each noun. Mark an S above it if it is singular or a P if it is plural.

    The mother goose led the goslings across the busy street.

2. Underline the main verb in this sentence. Circle the helping verb.

    The wasps had stung the little girl four times.

3. **When a plural noun ends in -s, add the apostrophe after the -s to make it possessive (-s').** Add a plural possessive to complete the sentences.

    The twins are cold. Will you get the _____ blankets?

    The girls have many books.
    The _____ books are on the shelf.

4. Write the past progressive form of the verb *call*.

    I _____ _____ all my friends to invite them to the party.

5. What is missing from this fragment?

    Is going to the splash park   subject   verb

    Correctly rewrite it as a complete sentence. Include proper capitalization and punctuation.

    _____

6. **A brand name is a proper noun. Always capitalize brand names.**

   Rewrite the product brand names on the line.

   Dad drives a ford and Mom drives a chevy.

   _____

7. Add a comma before the coordinating conjunction in this compound sentence.

   Our swim team won a trophy for diving and we almost won one for the 100 meter backstroke.

8. Circle the meaning of the underlined word.

   We could see snow on the <u>pinnacle</u> of the mountain, but we knew we could never climb to that high point.

         valley   peak   pyramid

9. Underline the word that means "use badly." Check in a dictionary or thesaurus.

        misuse   reuse   useless   useful

10. Write a contraction that can replace the underlined words.

    Jason <u>could not</u> get the car started.

    _____

Lesson #10

1. Add an *apostrophe* to make these plurals possessive.

   This is the girls dormitory.

   These animals cages are very clean and spacious.

2. **Irregular verbs do not end in *-ed* and change form when used with helping verbs.** You will find a list of irregular verbs in the *Help Pages* in the back of this book. Choose the correct verb.

   Aunt Betty was surprised to see how the children had (growed / grew / grown)!

3. ***Which* refers to things.** Choose the correct relative pronoun.

   The clock, _____ is an antique, is still ticking.

   which   whom   who

4. **A number that describes a noun is an adjective.** Circle the adjectives that tell *number*.

   Four monkeys played with three rings at the zoo.

   Five seats were empty on the bus.

5. **A preposition shows how words in a sentence are related. A noun or a pronoun comes after a preposition.**

   Example: My dog ran <u>over</u> the bridge.

   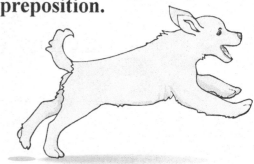

   Circle the preposition.

   He jumped into my arms.

6. Insert a comma and quotation marks.

    Cory asked How many more days until my birthday?

7. Use the proofreader's symbols for "check spelling" and "add something" to fix this sentence. Write the sentence correctly.

    We are going to a pupet show morning.

_____

8. What is the meaning of the word *heart* in this sentence?

    Grandma puts so much heart into all she does for us.

    feeling   love   kindness   all of these

Read these sentences and use them to answer items 9 and 10.

    A) Marshal did his <u>report</u> on insects.

    B) The army private was told to <u>report</u> for duty.

9. In which sentence is *report* a verb that means "to present oneself"?

                        A   B

10. In which sentence is *report* a noun that means "a written paper"?

                        A   B

Lesson #11

1. **A collective noun names a group, but it is singular. The verb must agree.** Choose the correct verb.

   The <u>company</u> (is / are) moving its office.

   A <u>pack</u> of wolves (hunts / hunt).

2. **A subject pronoun is used as the subject of a sentence. The subject pronouns are *I*, *you*, *he*, *she*, *it*, *we*, *you* (plural), and *they*.**

   Write a pronoun as the subject of this sentence.

   _____ put seed in the bird feeder.

3. Write the <u>present progressive form</u> of the verb *watch*.

   Susan _____ her favorite TV program.

4. When the subject pronoun is *he*, *she*, or *it*, add -*s* (or -*es*) to the present tense verb. Choose the correct verb.

   He (mix / mixes) a bowl of cake batter.

   It (fill / fills) two round cake pans.

   She (offer / offers) to bake a second cake.

5. **A prepositional phrase begins with a preposition and ends with a noun (or pronoun).** Look at the prepositional phrase that is underlined. Find the preposition and circle it.

   Jasmine planted petunias <u>along the sidewalk</u>.

   Ricky ate candy <u>during the movie</u>.

6. **Always capitalize the names of holidays.**

   Underline the words that should be capitalized.
   Rewrite the words correctly on the line.

   julia and i can't wait for the fireworks on
   the fourth of july!

   _____

7. What type of sentence is this?

   Is it time for the movie to begin?

   _____ imperative   _____ exclamatory

   _____ interrogative   _____ declarative

8. Write the words with prefixes.

   re + play _____

   un + do _____

9. Choose the synonym for the underlined word.

   Cedric knew how to <u>mend</u> his torn jeans.

       clean   replace   hide   repair

10. Underline the metaphor.

   The tiger was a bolt of lightning as it went after its prey.

Lesson #12

1. Write the irregular plurals.

    calf _____   thief _____   half _____

2. **When writing a letter, capitalize the first word and any proper nouns in the greeting and closing.** Rewrite these correctly.

    my dearest amelia, _____

    with hugs and kisses, frankie _____

3. Underline the relative pronoun. Draw an arrow to the antecedent.

    The puppy that had sad eyes was the first to be chosen.

4. **Adjectives tell *size*, *shape*, *age*, *color*, and *number*. A word that states an opinion about a noun is also an adjective.** Underline the adjective that states an opinion in each sentence.

    Grandma always bakes delicious cookies.

    The beautiful flowers were a thoughtful gift.

5. Draw a line through the fragment.

    This summer I am going to camp. Fishing and horseback riding. I always make new friends and I'm sad when the week is over.

    Rewrite the fragment as a complete thought.

    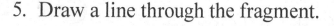
    _____

6. Use the proofreader's symbols for "make lower case" and "take something out" to fix this sentence. (See *Help Pages* if needed.)

   Calvin is eager to go to the the Beach.

7. Insert a comma and a coordinating conjunction.

   No one answered the phone _____ I left a message.

8 – 10. Choose a word to complete each proverb.

   cooks   glass   wheel   trash   book

   People who live in _____ houses shouldn't throw stones.

   The squeaky _____ gets the grease.

   Too many _____ spoil the broth.

   Don't judge a _____ by its cover.

   Select one of the above proverbs and explain its meaning in your own words.

   _____

   _____

   _____

Lesson #13

1. **The helping verb and the main verb are the entire verb in each sentence.** Underline the past tense helping verb and circle the main verb in each sentence.

   She had pedaled ten miles.

   The class had learned multiplication last year.

2. Complete the sentence with the <u>past progressive form</u> of the verb *look*.

   Robin _____ _____ all over for her silver locket.

3. Match each sentence with the way *can* is used.

   A) Rocky has learned the position and can play goalie.
   B) Jack can ride his bike to school when the weather is nice.

   _____ is able to

   _____ has permission to

4. **A prepositional phrase begins with a preposition and ends with a noun (or pronoun).** Underline the prepositional phrase in each sentence. Circle the preposition.

   Madison found her slippers under her bed.

   Corbin placed his supplies inside the box.

5. Underline the conjunction that joins two complete thoughts.

   The girls went to the mall, and they met friends at the movies on Saturday.

6. Choose the correct word.

Marsha is (to / too / two) years older than Darius.

7. **The names of the months and the days of the week begin with a capital letter. Their abbreviations also begin with a capital letter.**

Rewrite each day, month, and abbreviation correctly.

april	tues.	monday	dec.	aug.	sun.

8. Write the irregular plurals.

tooth _____   scarf _____   self _____

9. **A compound sentence has more than one complete thought. It uses a coordinating conjunction.** See the *Help Pages* for a list of coordinating conjunctions. Which is a compound sentence?

_____ Marcy bought snacks and drinks for the party.

_____ Everyone came on time, but Juliet had to leave early.

10. What is the meaning of the idiom?

Johnny really seems to have a <u>chip on his shoulder.</u>

A) A classmate secretly put a potato chip there.
B) Johnny always seems troubled.
C) He is walking with one shoulder lower than the other.

Lesson #14

1. **Object pronouns replace nouns as direct objects. Direct objects are in the predicate because they receive the action of a verb. The object pronouns are *me, you, him, her, it, us, you* (plural), and *them.*** Underline the object pronoun in the predicate of this sentence.

   Mom will drive me to softball practice.

2. Insert commas where they are needed.

   Your chores are to make your bed take out the trash and set the table.

3. **A noun may be described by more than one adjective. An adjective that states an *opinion* usually comes <u>before</u> an adjective that tells *color*.**

   Underline the adjective that tells *color*, and circle the adjective that states an *opinion* in each sentence.

   The lovely green leaves grew toward the sun.

   Jayden observed the strange yellow insect with his lens.

4. Choose the correct relative pronoun. Circle the antecedent.

   The shoes _____ Dorothy wore were red and sparkly.

        that   whose   who

5. **Relative adverbs tell *where*, *when*, and *why*. They begin a group of words that tells more about a noun.** Circle the relative adverb. Underline the noun it tells about.

   That is the hospital where you were born.

6. Use the proofreader's symbols for "make lower case" and "check spelling" to correct this sentence. (See *Help Pages* if needed.)

    Wood you like to come to my House for diner?

    Rewrite the sentence correctly.

    _____

7. Add a comma before the coordinating conjunction.

    I already have my bathing suit but Jackie thinks I should bring a towel and sunscreen, too.

8. What is the meaning of the word *muscle* in this sentence?

    You can finish the job in an hour if you put a little <u>muscle</u> into it.

    A) body tissue   C) weight lifting
    B) effort   D) all of these

9 – 10. Finish the chart by adding a cause or effect to each line.

Cause	Effect
	I got stung by a wasp.
I overslept.	

Lesson #15

1. Write the plurals of these words.

   fox _____   latch _____   brush _____

2. Complete the sentence with the <u>future progressive form</u> of the verb *shop.*

   Becky _____ _____ _____ for new supplies this weekend.

3. Which sentence uses *can* in place of "permission to?"

   _____ Mom says I <u>can</u> stay after school for play practice.

   _____ Kara <u>can</u> play second base better than any other player.

4. Find and underline two prepositional phrases in this sentence. Circle the prepositions.

   Please leave the cookies on the table and put the drinks in the cooler.

5. Underline the correct word.

   Grandma lives (here / hear) during the winter.

6. Use the prefix *dis-* to write an antonym for *respected*.

_____

7. Underline the metaphor.

   The driver was boiling mad.

8. **Capitalize the first, last, and all important words in the title of a book, magazine, movie, website, poem, and short story.**

   Circle all the words that should be capitalized.

   a cricket in times square is on my summer reading list.

9. What is the meaning of the underlined idiom?

   Emily knew the math problem was the hardest she'd ever seen, but she thought she would <u>give it a shot</u>.

   A) skip it
   B) use a calculator
   C) try

10. **A run-on sentence combines two or more sentences together as one sentence. A run-on sentence should be rewritten as two or more sentences.** Look at this run-on sentence. Rewrite it as two sentences.

    I have the cutest dogs in the world their names are Madison and Wilson.

_____

_____

Lesson #16

1. **To show that a person, place, or thing owns something, use a *possessive pronoun*. The possessive pronouns are *my*, *your*, *his*, *her*, *its*, and *their*.**

   Underline the possessive pronouns.

   She sewed his button back onto the shirt for him.

   Don and Laura sold lemonade to raise money for their school.

2. Underline the relative adverb.

   You will be a good cook when you get older.

3. What type of sentence is this?

   The first day of summer is June 21.

   _____ imperative

   _____ exclamatory

   _____ interrogative

   _____ declarative

4. Find the preposition in the prepositional phrase and write it on the line.

   Aunt Carol likes her tea with sugar and milk. _____

5. Choose the correct homophone.

   My aunt and uncle love (there / their) new house.

6. Insert a comma and quotation marks.

   Mark said I think I broke my arm!

7. Write the plural form of each word.

   peach _____   wolf _____   child _____

8. **A noun may be described by more than one adjective. An adjective that states an *opinion* usually comes <u>before</u> an adjective that tells *shape*.**

   Underline the adjective that tells *shape* and circle the adjective that states an *opinion*.

   Mary Sue squeezed through the dim rectangular opening in the cave.

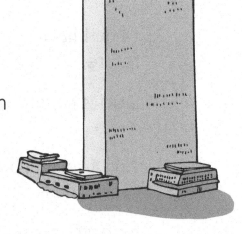

9. Circle the meaning of the underlined word.

   The large <u>structure</u> cast a shadow on the sidewalk below.

        entrance   building   groundhog

10. Which two words mean almost the same? Check in a dictionary or thesaurus.

      immoral   uneducated   illiterate   mismatch

Lesson #17

1. **Possessive pronouns may appear before a noun. The singular possessive pronouns are** *my, your, her, his, its.* **The plural possessive pronouns are** *our, your, their.* Use a possessive pronoun to replace the underlined words in the following sentences.

   The robin built <u>the robin's</u>
   nest out of small twigs.   _____

   Pamela called <u>Pamela's</u> friend
   to ask about the homework.   _____

   Benny and George left <u>Benny's</u>
   <u>and George's</u> sled outside.   _____

2. Underline the <u>progressive tense verb</u>. Write past, present, or future.

   Dad is painting my room a bright green color. _____

3. Add a comma before the coordinating conjunction.

   Richard is good at basketball but Mary thinks volleyball is her best sport.

4. Underline the prepositional phrase and write the preposition on the line.

   Our street lost power during the storm. _____

5. Use a dictionary to find the meaning of the words *celestial bodies.*

   objects in space   people who study space

   clouds and angels   none of these

6. **Can is a special verb that shows *willingness* to do the action of the main verb. It also suggests the *possibility* of doing the action of the main verb.** Underline the helping verb and the main verb. Then, write willingness or possibility to describe how the word *can* is used.

   I can get the order when the food is ready. _____

   You can hurt yourself if you go barefoot.   _____

7. Circle the simple subject and underline the simple predicate in this sentence.

   We read a story about the first Africans in America.

8. What is the meaning of the underlined idiom?

   I chose the designer shirt from the catalog, but Mom said I couldn't get it because it <u>cost an arm and a leg</u>.

   A) is cheap
   B) is expensive
   C) is stylish

9. Underline the words that should be capitalized.

   jeremy and i borrowed the book *hatchet* from mrs. ross.

10. Choose the meaning of the underlined word.

    Maria gave herself a quick <u>glance</u> in the mirror before she ran out the door to catch the bus.

    smile   comb   look   sleepy

Lesson #18

1. An adjective modifies a noun. An adverb modifies a

    _____.

2. For each sentence, circle the pronoun and underline its antecedent.

    Mrs. Pulaski asked Randy to play the piano for her.

    Slice the pizza while it is still hot.

    The classes wrote thank you notes and the principal mailed them.

3. Underline the relative adverb.

    I will be sad when you go to camp.

4. Underline the two things being compared in this simile.

    Grandma says Mark eats like a horse.

5. **An adjective that states an *opinion* usually comes <u>before</u> an adjective that tells *age*.** Underline the adjective that tells *age* and circle the adjective that states an *opinion* in each sentence.

    The noisy younger children played on the equipment.

    Brent carefully washed his shiny new bike.

6. Insert quotation marks to correct this sentence.

What time will you be home from work? asked Jeanne.

7. When a word ends in a consonant plus *y*, usually change the *y* to *i* and add *es* to make the plural. Make these words plural.

party _____   library _____   sky _____

8. Choose the word with the most negative meaning.

We were given a (skimpy / small / light) serving of dessert.

9. Use prefixes to write words with the following meanings.

not buttoned - _____

write again - _____

10. Draw a line through the fragment.

My friend, Andrea, takes gymnastics and dance lessons.
Competitions too. She has received many medals for her performances.

Rewrite the fragment as a complete thought.

_____

_____

Lesson #19

1. Choose the correct past tense verb.

   Olivia and Michael (was / were / been) late for soccer practice.

   Hailey had (tear / tore / torn) the page out of her notebook.

2. Circle the coordinating conjunction that joins two complete thoughts in each sentence. Underline each complete thought.

   I want to buy a new video game, so I am saving my money.

   Jason wanted to go on the trip, but he missed the bus.

3. Underline the <u>progressive tense</u> verb. Tell whether it is in the past, present, or future.

   Jeff will be bringing his dogs with him to the park.

        past   present   future

4. Use two proofreader's symbols to make corrections in each sentence.

   They left the Cover off of the pool

   Did you no that tonight there will be full moon?

5. Correctly rewrite both sentences from item 4.

   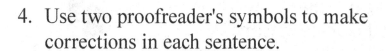

   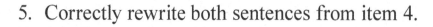

6. Underline the prepositional phrase in this sentence.

    Hope received a package from her friend.

    Write the preposition on the line.   _____

7. You can combine short sentences to make one compound sentence. Use a coordinating conjunction to combine these sentences. Don't forget to insert the comma properly.

    Dora put on her helmet. She rode her bike to school.

    _____

    _____

8. Choose a synonym for the underlined word.

    Raking leaves made her <u>sleepy</u>.

    awake   sick   nervous   drowsy

9. Underline the effect.

    The school was closed because there was no electricity.

10. Choose the meaning of the underlined word.

    Mrs. Gruber had <u>previously</u> given us new books and pencils.

    freely   earlier   supplies   later

Lesson #20

1. Choose the correct future tense verb.

    The postal carrier (will come / had come) before noon.

    Anthony (will run / had run) in the race tomorrow.

2. Write the irregular plural possessive noun.

    That _____ store carries clothing for men of all ages.
              (men)

    The _____ section of the library is so cozy!
              (children)

3. Insert a relative adverb.

    This is the same place _____ I saw you last week.

4. **An adjective that tells *size* usually comes <u>before</u> an adjective that tells *shape*.** Underline the adjective that tells *size* and circle the adjective that tells *shape* in each sentence.

    Mom put the soup in the large round container.

    I keep my valuables in a small oval box under my pillow.

5. Write this run-on as two complete sentences.

    We tied up the boat at the dock we saw a big storm was coming.

    _____

    _____

6. Use the proofreader's symbols for "make capital" and "check spelling" to make corrections to this sentence.

   We went to the shedd aquarium last Saterday.

7. Add a comma before the coordinating conjunction.

   Shaundra got an A on her test so her mother made a special dinner.

8. Write F for formal English or I for informal English.

   _____ Jake was hurt when he fell off his snowboard.

   _____ Ouch! That belly flop had to really hurt.

9. Choose the correct word.

   Nora didn't want to get her (hare / hair) cut.

10. What is the meaning of the underlined idiom?

    We were so surprised when Uncle Mark showed up <u>out of the blue</u> for dinner last night.

    A) late

    B) wearing blue

    C) without warning

Lesson #21

1. Choose the correct past tense verb.

   The girls had (drive / drove / driven) the go-cart on the sidewalk.

   Sonia had (write / wrote / written) an email to her grandmother.

2. Underline the progressive tense verb. Tell whether it is in the past, present, or future.

   Andrea will be arriving at the airport soon.

   past   present   future

3. Match each sentence with the way in which *can* is being used.

   A) You <u>can</u> get sunburned unless you wear sunscreen.
   B) I <u>can</u> help you fix your bike.

   _____ willingness to do something

   _____ possibility of something

4. Find the prepositions in the prepositional phrases and write them on the line.

   Celine babysits for a family who lives near the school. _____

5. Use the proofreader's symbols for "make capital" and "make lower case" to fix this sentence.

   Casey will visit aunt sarah next Weekend.

6. Add quotation marks.

Are we going camping this
weekend? asked Monique.

7. Insert a comma and a coordinating
conjunction to combine the complete
thoughts into a compound sentence.

Andrew Jackson was very poor as a child _____ he

became President of the United States.

8 – 10. Write some similes of your own. Complete each of the following.

quick as / like a _____

pretty as / like a _____

angry as / like a _____

"cuddly as a cactus"
(Ouch!)

Lesson #22

1. Look at the pronouns *I* and *me*. Are they in the <u>subject</u> or the <u>predicate</u>? Circle the pronoun that is correct in each sentence.

   (I / me) played hide and seek with the children.

   Louis found my brother and (I / me) right away.

2. One of the possessives in this sentence is incorrect. Cross it out and write it correctly on the line.

   Nicoles' brother lost my sister's watch.   _____

3. Underline the relative adverb.

   Let us know the time when you will be baking.

4. **An adjective that tells *age* usually comes <u>before</u> an adjective that tells *color*.** Underline the adjective that tells *age* and circle the adjective that tells *color* in each sentence.

   Our team is wearing new purple uniforms this year.

   Marisol found Dad's old brown mitt in the garage.

5. Underline the meaning of the word *inequality*. Check in a dictionary or thesaurus.

   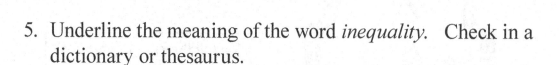

   unending   equal   not equal   even

6. Use proofreader's symbols to show words that should be capitalized. Underline the book title.

    miss grey read us the book charlotte's web.

7. Add –*ing* to these words.

    jog _____   ship _____

8. Match.

    formal English   informal English

    When I . . .   **I use...**

    write a note to my friend   _____

    write a research report   _____

9. Write S if the words are synonyms. Write A if they are antonyms.

    _____ hurry / rush

    _____ rarely / frequently

10. Rewrite this run-on sentence as two complete thoughts.

    We are making cookies would you like to help?

    _____

    _____

Lesson #23

1. **Single reflexive pronouns end in** *self.* **Plural reflexive pronouns end in** *selves.* Circle the reflexive pronoun and draw an arrow to the noun or pronoun that it refers to.

   Monroe studied himself in the mirror.

   Clay and I photographed ourselves in front of the statue.

2. Choose the possessive pronoun.

   The tree had a hole in (it's / its) trunk.

3. Complete the sentence. Choose the <u>present progressive form</u> of the verb.

   Kellie _____ in the final gymnastics competition.

   will be performing   performed   is performing

4. **Should you use the preposition** *between* **or** *among*? **Use** *between* **when speaking or writing about just two items. Use** *among* **when speaking or writing about more than two.**

   Choose the best word to complete this sentence.

   The girls had to choose (between / among) mini golf or roller skating.

5. Choose the correct word.

   Moira said I could come along, (to / too / two).

6. Add a comma and quotation marks to correct this sentence.

   The teacher shouted It's time to come inside!

7. Underline each complete thought in this compound sentence.

   I want to ride that roller coaster, but I'm not tall enough.

8 – 10. Finish the chart by adding a cause or effect to each line. One has been done for you.

Cause	Effect
It was raining.	Mary took an umbrella to work.
	The kitchen was very cold.
The puppy was left alone too long.	
The teacher wasn't feeling well.	

Lesson #24

1. Put a line under the adjectives that compare.

    Wear the warmest winter coat you can find because today is even colder than yesterday.

2. Underline the relative adverb.

    Let's go to the store where they sell Italian baked goods.

3. The word *could* is a helping verb. It means "was able to" (past tense). *Could* also suggests the possibility of the main verb.

    Match each sentence to the way in which *could* is being used.

    _____ was able   A) If you hurry, you could make the 5 o'clock train.

    _____ possibility   B) Sasha could run faster than anyone else on the team.

4. **An adjective that tells *size* usually comes <u>before</u> an adjective that tells *age*.** Underline the adjective that tells *size* and circle the adjective that tells *age* in each sentence.

    The tiny young tomato plants needed water.

    The giant old oak tree cast a long shadow in the yard.

5. Use the proofreader's symbol for "make capital" to correct this sentence.

    The cat's real name is lady harrington.

6. Add a comma before the coordinating conjunction.

   I like carrots but golden beets are my favorite.

7. Read each sentence. Write F if you would use formal English. Write I if you would use informal English.

   _____ Speaking with the principal

   _____ Giving an oral book report

   _____ Talking with friends in the lunchroom

   _____ Playing video games with your brother

8. Write S if the words are synonyms. Write A if they are antonyms.

   _____ sleepy / drowsy

   _____ modern / ancient

9. Underline each complete thought in this compound sentence.

   Henry was lost, and he didn't know how to find his way home.

10. Match these prefixes with their meanings.

   re-   dis-   pre-   mis-

   badly _____   before _____

   not _____   again _____

Lesson #25

1. Underline the future tense verb.

   The sunflowers will grow to be eight feet high by the end of summer.

2. Insert commas where they are needed.

   Shauna watered the flowers cut the grass and trimmed the shrubs.

3. Cross out the fragment.

   Alaska is the largest state in size. Few people live there. Twice as large as Texas. Alaska has many islands.

   Add some words to the fragment to make a complete thought.

   _____

4. **An adjective that tells *shape* usually comes <u>before</u> an adjective that tells *color*.** Underline the adjective that tells *shape* and circle the adjective that tells *color* in each sentence.

   They danced on a curved brown stage.

   Paul Revere wore a triangular black hat.

5. Complete the sentence. Choose the <u>past progressive form</u> of the verb.

   Paul _____ in a golf tournament on Kiawah Island.

   will be playing   plays   was playing

6. Correct any capitalization errors on the line.

   our team will play the giants at jackson park on sunday.

   _____

7. **If a word ends in -*e* and you want to add a suffix that begins with a vowel, drop the -*e* before adding the suffix.**

   Add -*er* and -*est* to the word.

   cute   _____   _____

8. Underline the two things being compared in this simile.

   The snow was as white as the clouds.

9 – 10. Finish the chart by adding a cause or effect to each line.

Cause	Effect
The road was closed.	
	I had to wait outside in the rain.

Lesson #26

1. Underline the adverbs that compare.

   I got up earlier than I usually do, and I got so much done.

   My kite flies higher than the trees!

2. Add an apostrophe to make these plurals possessive.

   Don't bump into the birds nest!

   The girls sweaters were all over the floor.

3. Underline the relative adverb.

   You can go bowling when you finish your chores.

4. **An adjective that states an *opinion* always comes <u>after</u> an adjective that tells *number*.** Complete the sentence by writing the adjectives in the correct order.

   warm   sixteen

   Kevin tried on _____ _____ sweaters before selecting a green and blue one.

5. Draw a line through the fragment.

   Tropical rain forests are divided into four parts. Many different kinds of plants live in the rain forest. And many animals too. The rain forest gives us food and medicine.

   Rewrite the fragment as a complete thought.

   _____

   _____

6. Insert quotation marks.

   Barbara asked, Has anyone seen my slippers?

7. Underline the complete subject and double underline the complete predicate of this sentence.

   Allison turned in her social studies report.

8. Write what the friends are saying. Use informal English.

9. Are these words *synonyms* or *antonyms*?   dull   interesting

                    synonyms   antonyms

10. Is the underlined part of the sentence a cause or effect?

    <u>The other team didn't show up</u>, so we won the game.

                    cause   effect

Lesson #27

1. Put a line under the adjectives that compare.

   That is not only the fastest car on the track today, it is also the most beautiful.

2. Complete the sentence. Choose the <u>past progressive form</u> of the verb.

   We _____ lots of hot dogs at "Dollar Dog Night" at the ball game.

   > were eating   ate   will be eating

3. How is the word *could* used in the following sentence?

   We could go to the park if it stops raining.

   > possibility of something   permission to

4. Choose the best word to complete this sentence.

   At Baby Cakes Bakery, I chose (between / among) lemon, mint chocolate, red velvet, and carrot cake cupcakes.

5. Cross out the fragment.

   Seals push themselves through the water with their rear flippers. They use their front flippers for steering. The front flippers are short. With sharp claws.

   Add some words to the fragment to make a complete thought or combine it with another sentence.

6. Add a comma and quotation marks to correct this sentence.

   The coach instructed Run as fast as you can to first base!

7. Draw a line between the subject and the predicate.

   Regina brought a plate of brownies to her neighbor.

8. What is the meaning of the underlined idiom?

   I studied for the science test last night, but today I <u>drew a blank</u>.

   A) couldn't remember the answers
   B) drew pictures
   C) filled in the blanks

9. Are you feeling *perturbed* or *serene*? Circle one and then look up the words in a dictionary. Choose the synonyms that go with each word.

   perturbed _____   serene _____

       A) disturbed   B) relaxed   C) calm   D) worried

10. Choose the meaning of the underlined word.

   Jennifer was very <u>flexible</u> since she had been practicing gymnastics for seven years.

       freely   bendable   strong   stiff

Lesson #28

1. Choose the correct past tense verb.

   Izzy and Jackie (do / done / did) their homework last night.

   Tyler (fall / fell / fallen) from the top of his bunk bed.

   Mr. McAlister (shook / shake / shaked) the paint can.

2. Underline the relative adverb.

   The whole city lost power when the storm came through.

3. Complete the sentence by writing the adjectives in the correct order. See the *Help Pages* if you are not sure which adjective should come first.

   four   yellow

   I watched _____ _____ buses turn around on the school playground.

4. Underline the prepositional phrases. Circle the prepositions.

   We took a walk along the beach.

   The little girl hid behind the door.

5. Choose the correct word.

   No one (new / knew) if the (new / knew) student had arrived.

6. Add a comma before the coordinating conjunction.

   This camping trip will be fun but I hope no one gets poison ivy this year!

7. Use *-less* to write a word that means "the opposite of hopeful."

   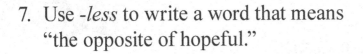

8. Use prefixes that mean "not" to write words with these meanings.

   not possible - _____ (im-)

   not agree - _____ (dis-)

9. Are the words *familiar* and *strange* synonyms or antonyms?

   synonyms   antonyms

10. Correctly write any words that should be capitalized.

    my friends and i took our dogs to the park on main street.

    _____

Lesson #29

1. Underline all the adjectives.

    The blue smoke bellowed up from the large bonfire filling the air with a pungent odor.

    The jar of homemade cookies was hidden in the dark, windowless room.

2. Underline the relative adverb.

    We love to shop at the market where the smells are so delicious.

3. Complete the sentence. Write the <u>present progressive form</u> of the verb *attend*.

    Ella and Macy _____ soccer camp in Ohio this summer.

4. The word *could* expresses less certainty than *can*. Choose the verb that expresses the right amount of certainty for each sentence.

    Yes, I (could / can) give you directions to my home.

    Maybe Sophie (could / can) bring a dessert to the picnic.

5. Cross out the fragment. Underline the sentence with no errors.

    We are studying whales in science class. And also dolphins. science class is fun!

6. Add quotation marks to correct this sentence.

   What time does the pool open? asked Monica.

7. Underline the subject. Write the verb.

   She is on the boat.

   _____

8. Underline the effect.

   The little girl is crying because she lost her teddy bear.

9. Choose two antonyms.

        careful   ordinary   useless   rare

10. What is the meaning of the underlined idiom?

    The toddler looked around to make sure everyone was watching, and then began to <u>cry crocodile tears</u>.

    A) wipe her tears

    B) pretend to be upset

    C) feed the crocodile

Lesson #30

1. Fill in an adverb to complete this sentence.

   Brandon _____ washed
   the car.

2. Complete the sentence. Write the <u>present progressive form</u> of the
   verb *plant*.

   Grandma _____ tomatoes and peppers
   in her garden.

3. Complete the sentence by writing the adjectives in the correct order.

   square   two   small

   The _____ _____ _____ dice tumbled
   across the game board.

4. Underline the prepositional phrase and circle the preposition in each
   sentence.

   The snow covered the tops of the mountains.

   Henry sat between his two friends.

5. Choose the correct words.

   (They're / There) was no way to know
   if (their / there) bus would be back on
   time.

6. Which of these should begin with a capital letter?

    A) days of the week and months of the year
    B) countries of the world
    C) first, last, and important words in titles of books
    D) all of the above

7. Add a comma before the coordinating conjunction.

Are you having a fun summer or are you ready for school to start again?

8. Look at these words. What does the prefix mean?

      prewash   preheat   preview

_____

9. Underline two things being compared in this metaphor.

The umbrella was a roof over her head.

10. Draw a line between the subject and the predicate.

Playful monkeys climbed all over each other.

Standards-Based
ENGLISH GRAMMAR
& Mechanics

4

Help Pages

Help Pages

Parts of Speech - Nouns

A **common noun** names a person, place, thing, or idea. A **proper noun** names a particular person, place, thing, or idea. A proper noun begins with a capital letter. Nouns may be singular or plural.

Some of the Functions of Nouns

Subject	The subject is whom or what the sentence is about. *Example*: <u>Tom</u> likes to play piano.
Direct Object	A direct object receives the action of the verb. *Example*: Tom plays the <u>piano</u>. To find the DO, ask: Tom plays what?
Possessive	A possessive noun shows ownership and usually modifies another noun. *Examples*: <u>Mr. Gore's</u> class uses <u>Tom's</u> piano.

Parts of Speech - Pronouns

A **pronoun** takes the place of a noun. The noun that the pronoun is referring to is called the **antecedent**. The antecedent is in the same sentence or a recent, earlier sentence; occasionally, an antecedent is not specifically named. It is implied, or "understood."

Examples: The <u>puppy</u> is in <u>its</u> pen.
("<u>its</u> pen" refers to the puppy's pen, so "puppy" is the antecedent.)
<u>It</u> has been raining all day.
(There is no clear antecedent, but we know "it" refers to the weather.)

Personal Pronouns

Subject Pronouns	Used as the subject of a sentence or clause *Singular*: I, you, he/she, it *Plural*: we, you, they
Object Pronouns	Used as an object; found in the predicate of a sentence *Singular*: me, you, him/her, it *Plural*: us, you, them
Possessive Pronouns	Used to show ownership; modify nouns *Singular*: my, mine*, your, yours*, his*, her, hers*, its* *Plural*: our, ours*, your, yours*, their, theirs*, whose * These can stand alone.
Relative Pronouns	Connect incomplete thoughts to complete thoughts (that, which, who, whom, whoever, whomever, whichever) *Example*: She is the one <u>who</u> won the prize.

Parts of Speech - Conjunctions

Coordinating Conjunctions	Join two equal elements or two complete thoughts Use the acronym FANBOYS (for, and, nor, but, or, yet, so) to remember them. *Example*: We swam in the ocean <u>and</u> roasted hot dogs over the fire.

Help Pages

Parts of Speech - Adjectives

Adjectives modify nouns or pronouns. Adjectives tell *how many*, *what color*, *how big*, *how small*, *what kind*, and so on.   ***Example***: He was a <u>tall</u> man.
A proper adjective begins with a capital letter.   ***Example***: <u>Siberian</u> Husky
An **article** is a special type of adjective (a, an, the).   ***Example***: Throw Jack <u>the</u> ball.

Conventional Adjective Patterns

There is an accepted pattern to the order of speaking or writing types of adjectives. This table shows types of adjectives and the order in which they would normally be spoken or written.

Number	Observation or opinion	Physical properties				Noun
		Size	Shape	Age	Color	
seven	beautiful	large			blue	marbles
dozen		small	oval			eggs
a	slow			old		turtle
couple	smart			young		toddlers

Parts of Speech - Verbs

Action   Shows an action
Example: A stunt man <u>performs</u> dangerous feats.
             The symphony <u>performs</u> every Sunday.

Being   Does not show action; shows what the subject is; a state of being
Examples: is, are, was, were, be, am, being, been

Helping   Pairs with a main verb to form a verb phrase
Examples: is, are, was, were, be, am, being, been, might, could, should, would, can, do, does, did, may, must, will, shall, have, has, had

Verb Tense

Verb tense tells the time when the action or condition of the verb occurs.

Simple Verb Tenses

Present   The action is occurring now or is unchanging.

The house <u>is</u> new. (singular subject)
The boys <u>swim</u>. (plural)

Past   The action was started and completed in the past.

The clock <u>stopped</u>. (singular subject)
The buses <u>ran</u>. (plural)

Future   The action will not start until the future.

The snow <u>will fall</u>. (singular subject)
The lakes <u>will freeze</u>. (plural)

Progressive Verb Tenses

A main verb that ends in *–ing* works with a helping verb to form the progressive tense.

Present   She <u>is sleeping</u>.
             They <u>are eating</u>.

Past   She <u>was sleeping</u>.
             They <u>were eating</u>.

Future   She <u>will be sleeping</u>.
             They <u>will be eating</u>.

Help Pages

Irregular Verbs

Present	Past	Use with *has, have*, or *had*	Present	Past	Use with *has, have*, or *had*
am/is/are	was/were	been	keep	kept	kept
begin	began	begun	make	made	made
blow	blew	blown	mistake	mistook	mistaken
break	broke	broken	ride	rode	ridden
bring	brought	brought	ring	rang	rung
build	built	built	say	said	said
choose	chose	chosen	shrink	shrank	shrunk
do	did	done	sing	sang	sung
draw	drew	drawn	speak	spoke	spoken
drink	drank	drunk	steal	stole	stolen
drive	drove	driven	stink	stank	stunk
eat	ate	eaten	swim	swam	swum
fall	fell	fallen	teach	taught	taught
fly	flew	flown	tear	tore	torn
freeze	froze	frozen	tell	told	told
get	got	gotten	think	thought	thought
grow	grew	grown	throw	threw	thrown
have	had	had	wear	wore	worn

Parts of Speech - Prepositions

Prepositions relate nouns or pronouns to other words in the sentence. A **prepositional phrase** begins with a preposition and ends with a noun or a pronoun.

Some Common Prepositions

about	around	by	into	out	under
above	before	down	near	outside	underneath
across	behind	during	nearby	over	until
after	below	except	next to	past	up
against	beneath	for	of	through	upon
along	beside	from	off	throughout	with
alongside	between	in	on	to	within
among	beyond	inside	onto	toward	without

Help Pages

Parts of Speech - Adverbs

Adverbs modify verbs, adjectives, or other adverbs.

Adverbs That Tell *When*

after	before	finally	never	often	until	while
always	earlier	later	next	sometimes	when	yesterday

Adverbs That Tell *How*

beautifully	eagerly	greedily	noisily	politely	quietly	selfishly
calmly	gracefully	loudly	perfectly	quickly	sadly	wildly

Adverbs That Tell *Where*

back	down	forward	in	outside	there	up
behind	everywhere	here	inside	somewhere	under	upward

Adverbs That Tell *To What Extent*

almost	completely	extremely	rather	scarcely	thoroughly	totally
also	entirely	quite	really	somewhat	too	very

Sentences

A **sentence** is a complete thought that includes a subject and a verb.

Features of a sentence:
1. begins with a capital letter
2. ends with punctuation/end mark
3. conveys a complete thought

Parts of a Sentence

Subject   The **simple subject** tells whom or what the sentence is about but does not include any words that describe the subject.

The **complete subject** includes the simple subject plus all of the modifiers that go with it.

Example: A few hungry **teenagers** devoured the pizza. *Teenagers* is the simple subject. *A few hungry teenagers* is the complete subject.

Predicate   The **simple predicate** is the verb.

The **complete predicate** is the verb plus the other words that say something about the subject – what the subject is or does.

Example: The tired children **climbed** slowly upstairs. *Climbed* is the simple predicate, or verb. *Climbed slowly upstairs* is the complete predicate.

The Four Sentence Types

Type	Other Name	Punctuation	Example:
declarative	statement	period	This is a sentence.
interrogative	question	question mark	Is this correct?
imperative	command/request	period	Please open the door.
exclamatory	exclamation	exclamation point	This is awesome!

Help Pages

Sentences (continued)

Fragments

A fragment is not a sentence because it does not express a complete thought. A fragment is missing either a subject or a verb.

Examples: The book that I read. (missing a verb)

Running down the street. (missing a subject)

Run-on Sentences

A run-on is two or more complete thoughts that run together without proper punctuation or conjunctions.

Examples:

Incorrect: The twins really wanted to ride the roller coaster there was a height requirement they were too short decided to ride the Ferris wheel instead.

Correct: The twins really wanted to ride the roller coaster. There was a height requirement, and they were too short. They decided to ride the Ferris wheel instead.

Sentence Structure	
Simple	**Parts**: subject and predicate only **Example**: We will hold a rally at the local park.
Compound	**Parts**: two or more complete thoughts **Joined by**: coordinating conjunction **Example**: There will be speeches in the morning, and we will play games in the afternoon.
Complex	**Parts**: one complete thought and one or more incomplete thoughts **Joined by**: subordinating conjunction **Example**: I took my umbrella because it was raining.

Punctuation	
Commas (,)	Use commas to separate words or phrases in a series. *Example*: Sun brought a coloring book, some crayons, and a pair of scissors.
	Use a comma to separate two independent clauses joined by a conjunction. *Example*: Dad works in the city, and he is a commuter.
	Use a comma to separate two words or two numbers when writing a date. *Example*: Friday, April 8, 2011
	Use a comma between the city and state in an address. *Examples*: Boston, MA Honolulu, Hawaii
	Use commas in greetings and closings of letters. *Examples*: Dear Mr. Clydesdale, Sincerely yours,
Apostrophe (')	Use an apostrophe to form a contraction or a possessive noun. *Examples*: I don't want to go. That was Sherry's little sister.
End marks	Use end punctuation for sentences. *See* **Four Sentence Types**.

Help Pages

Punctuation (continued)

Commas and Quotation Marks in Dialogue

Put quotation marks before and after the actual words that someone says. Quotation marks are like a frame around spoken words. Keep the end mark inside the quotes.
Example: She said, "We need to go now."

Capitalize the first word of a sentence in quotes.
Example: "Wait," said Sam, "the door is locked."

Use a comma or end mark before and after a quote.
Examples: "It's starting to rain!" Marcy exclaimed. Mickey replied, "Don't worry, you won't melt."

Do not use a comma at the end of a sentence within quotes if there is another end mark.
Example: "Grandma's here!" exclaimed Sasha.

Capitalization Rules

Capitalize the first word in a sentence, the pronoun *I*, proper nouns, and proper adjectives.

Capitalize names of days and months.

Capitalize holidays, product names, and geographic names. These are all proper nouns.

Capitalize the first, last and the important words in titles.
Example: *From the Mixed-Up Files of Mrs. Basil E. Frankweiler*

Other Types of Punctuation

Punctuating Titles

Show the title of a book, movie, play, television show, magazine, or website by using italics or by underlining it.

Examples:	*Sarah, Plain and Tall*	or	<u>Sarah, Plain and Tall</u>
	Peter and the Wolf	or	<u>Peter and the Wolf</u>
	Sesame Street	or	<u>Sesame Street</u>
	www.Toys.com	or	<u>www.Toys.com</u>

Put quotation marks around the title of a short work, such as a poem, song, short story, article or book chapter.
Examples: "Dreams" is a poem by Langston Hughes.

We sang "Jingle Bells" and many other winter songs.

"The Monkey's Paw" is a scary short story by W.W. Jacobs.

In <u>My Side of the Mountain</u>, by Jean Craighead George, one of the chapters is called "The Old, Old Tree."

Help Pages

Proofreader's Symbols		
Description	**Symbol**	**Example**
Make capital	≡	the car raced down the street.
Add something	∧	The car raced down street. the
Make lower case	/	The Car raced down the street.
Take something out	ℛ	The car raced down the the street.
Check spelling	(⬭) sp	The (cor) raced down the street.
Indent	¶	¶The car raced down the street.
Add end punctuation	⊙ ⧀ ⑦	The car raced down the street⊙

Greek and Latin Roots and Affixes and Their Meanings

Word Part	Meaning	Word Part	Meaning
able, ible	able to	hema	blood
anti	against	il	opposite
auto	self	im/in	not
bio	life	ion, tion, sion	forms noun from verb
centi	hundred	ment	state of
co	together	mono	one
dec	ten	ology	study of
dent	tooth	port	carry
dia	across	pre	before
dis	not	re	again
er	one who does	scrip	to write
ess	female	sent	feel
ful	full of	ty, ity	forms noun from adjective
graph, gram	written	un	not

Help Pages

Figurative Language

A **simile** is a way to describe something using a comparison. A simile compares two things using the words *like* or *as*.

Example: The baby is *as playful as a kitten*. (A baby is compared to a kitten.)

A **metaphor** compares two things but does not use *like* or *as*. It uses a form of the verb *be*.

Example: Joey is *a magnet for bad luck*. (He attracts bad luck.)

An **idiom** is a phrase whose meaning can't be understood from the literal meaning of the words.

Example: *This article is way over my head*. (This phrase could mean something is taller than I am. But when *over my head* is an idiom, it means something is too complicated to be understood.)

Examples: We bought a used car, and it's <u>a real lemon</u>!
(refers to a car that has many problems or doesn't run)

At first I was angry, but I <u>got over it</u>.
(refers to letting go of something that was upsetting)

An **adage** or **proverb** is a wise saying that most people think is true. It may give advice.

Example: *All that glitters is not gold*. (This saying warns us that something might seem valuable, but really is not valuable.)

Spelling Rules

Adding Prefixes

When adding a prefix or joining two words, do not change the spelling of the base word.

Examples: pre<u>cook</u>, <u>cook</u>book

Adding Suffixes that Begin with a Consonant

When adding a suffix that begins with a consonant, do not change the spelling of the base word.

Examples: joy + ful → joyful   wool + ly → woolly   agree + ment → agreement
            pain + ful → painful   sincere + ly → sincerely   govern + ment → government

Common Exceptions: argue + ment → argument   true + ly → truly   nine + th → ninth
                         judge + ment → judgment   due + ly → duly   awe + ful → awful

Adding Suffixes that Begin with a Vowel

When a word ends in a **vowel + y**, add a suffix without changing the spelling of the base word.

Examples: employ + er → employer   play + ing → playing
            gray + est → grayest   enjoy + ment → enjoyment

When a word ends in **silent -e**, usually drop the *-e* to add a suffix that begins with a vowel.

Examples: love + able → lovable

Help Pages

Spelling Rules (continued)

Adding Suffixes that Begin with a Vowel

When a word ends in a **consonant + y** pattern, usually change the *y* to *i* when adding a suffix.
     Examples: try + ed → tried   (ends in consonant + *y*; change the *y* to *i*)
 Do not change the *y* to *i* if the word ends in a vowel + *y* pattern or if the suffix is *ing*.
     Examples: destroy + ed → destroyed   (vowel + *y*)
              hurry + ing → hurrying   (consonant + *ing*)

When a one-syllable word ends in the **CVC pattern (consonant - vowel - consonant)**, usually double the final consonant to add a suffix that begins with a vowel.
     Examples: ship + ing → shipping   (suffix begins with a vowel)
              ship + ment → shipment   (suffix begins with a consonant)
              nut + y → nutty   (suffix is *y*)
 When a one-syllable word ends in the **CVC pattern**, and the final consonant is *s*, *x* or *w*, do not double the final consonant.
     Examples: mix + ing → mixing   box + ed → boxed   slow + er → slower

When a multi-syllable word ends in the **CVC pattern**, and the **accent is on the last syllable**, usually double the final consonant to add a suffix that begins with a vowel.   ***Example***:   commit + ing → committing   (suffix begins with a vowel)   ***Common Exception***:   prefer + able → preferable
Making Plurals
When a word **ends in s, x, z, ch, or sh** add -*es* to make the plural.   ***Examples***: tax → taxes; wish → wishes

Many words that **end in f or fe,** change the *f* or *fe* to -*ves*.
     Examples: life → lives; thief → thieves
 Other words that **end in f or ff** do not follow the rule for making plurals.
     Examples: cliff → cliffs; belief → beliefs

Irregular plural nouns have a completely different spelling in the plural form.

Common irregular plural nouns							
child	children	man	men	ox	oxen	tooth	teeth
louse	lice	mouse	mice	person	people	woman	women

Additional Spelling Rule
Place *i* before *e*, except after *c*, or when sounded like /ā/ as in neighbor and weigh.   ***Examples***: mischief   receive   eight
There are many exceptions to spelling rules. If you are not sure of the spelling of a word, use a dictionary to check.

Summer Solutions.

Minutes a Day–Mastery for a Lifetime!

Standards-Based
ENGLISH GRAMMAR
& Mechanics
4

Answers to Lessons

	Lesson #1		Lesson #2		Lesson #3
1	messages	**1**	Reggie China Boston	**1**	The <u>principal</u> will discover the (truth) I do not have a (fear) of <u>spiders</u> or <u>snakes</u>.
2	who	**2**	them it	**2**	<u>When George put his ivy plant near a sunny window</u>, it began to grow long leafy vines.
3	Polly bought ice-cream, nuts, candy, and cookies for the party.	**3**	A B	**3**	Example: about, around, by, down, beside (Answers will vary.)
4	The <u>sky</u> last night was as clear as a <u>bell</u>.	**4**	<u>liza</u> and <u>marcus</u> live on <u>brower road</u>.	**4**	close but no cigar at the last minute at the eleventh hour correct answer or idea that's the ticket not quite
5	talkative person	**5**	"Would you like to go camping with us?" Asher asked.	**5**	large fierce <u>dog</u> unknown <u>intruder</u>
6	It's its	**6**	<u>It is raining</u>, so <u>our baseball game will be cancelled</u>.	**6**	Monday, <u>mrs. sands</u> took <u>kay</u> and the boys to <u>ginger island</u>.
7	(Claire) <u>swims</u>	**7**	peaches mixes kisses	**7**	We are selling candy bars, popcorn, pretzels, and gum. Please bring your swimsuit, towel, sunscreen, and a snack to the pool party.
8	continuous, determined	**8**	impolite	**8**	cold snowy hot sunny
9	is frosting	**9** — **10**	Example: **Dear** Sarah, How are you? I miss you. I have been staying with my grandma in North Carolina. We go to the beach a lot. I'll be home in two weeks. Your friend, Kathy (Answers will vary.)	**9**	thrown
10	enormous			**10**	Example: She was absent yesterday because she had a cold. (Sentences will vary.)

Lesson #4		Lesson #5		Lesson #6	
1	gladly go	**1**	Mr. Torrez (gave)	**1**	B is A traveled A read A sings
2	Jamal has birds, cats, dogs, turtles, and hamsters as pets.	**2**	play adds	**2**	Example: 123 S. Main Street Anywhere, OH 44444 (Addresses will vary.)
3	Paulette wants a new bike, but she hasn't saved enough money.	**3**	not reasonable	**3**	useless
4	long (purple) (yellow) small (red)	**4**	was running	**4**	team that
5	who	**5**	verb Example: Five picnic baskets were sitting on the table. (Sentence will vary.)	**5**	She lost her ring.
6	is coming	**6**	suki i my i	**6**	We had Bagels and juice for breakfast⊙
7	What is this movie about?	**7**	dr. hanson is dentist. my, a, the... Dr. Hanson is my dentist. (Sentence will vary.)	**7**	It is nine o'clock at night, but it is still light outside.
8	sad or unhappy	**8**	quick speedy	**8**	narrow wide
9	i went with aunt mary to hear senator brown speak.	**9**	helpful	**9**	B
10	injuries babies	**10**	There was a power failure, so we had to light candles.	**10**	When it comes to work, Jason is a mule.

	Lesson #7		Lesson #8		Lesson #9
1	am is are being were been be was (Any order.)	1	has have	1	The mother goose led the goslings across the busy street.
2	past present future	2	There	2	(had) stung
3	will be walking	3	B A	3	twins' girls'
4	old (round) new (rectangular)	4	through on	4	was calling
5	hour our	5	⁋	5	subject Example: Our class is going to the splash park. (Sentence may vary.)
6	My family likes to go sailing on lake erie near sandusky bay. Lake Erie Sandusky Bay	6	who	6	Ford Chevy
7	It was the (bigest) snowstorm on record⊙ It was the biggest snowstorm on record.	7	Amanda asked, "May I borrow your camera?"	7	Our swim team won a trophy for diving, and we almost won one for the 100 meter backstroke.
8	cause	8	C	8	peak
9	expensive cheap	9	Examples: A) ...it blew the shutters off the house. B) Since so many students had the flu... (Answers will vary)	9	misuse
10	still	10		10	couldn't

	Lesson #10		Lesson #11		Lesson #12
1	girls' animals'	**1**	is hunts	**1**	calves thieves halves
2	grown	**2**	Example: We (Answer will vary.)	**2**	My dearest Amelia, With hugs and kisses, Frankie
3	which	**3**	is watching	**3**	puppy <u>that</u>
4	Four three five	**4**	mixes fills offers	**4**	delicious beautiful thoughtful
5	into	**5**	along during	**5**	~~Fishing and horseback riding.~~ Example: I will go fishing and horseback riding. (Sentence will vary.)
6	Cory asked, "How many more days until my birthday?"	**6**	<u>julia</u> and <u>i</u> can't wait for the fireworks on the <u>fourth</u> of <u>july</u>! Julia I Fourth July	**6**	Calvin is eager to go to the ~~the~~ Beach.
7	We are going to a puppet(sp) show morning. ∧this... We are going to a puppet show this morning.	**7**	✓ interrogative	**7**	No one answered the phone, so I left a message.
8	all of these	**8**	replay undo	**8** — **10**	glass wheel cooks book Example: The person who makes the most noise gets the attention. (The squeaky wheel gets the grease.) (Proverb and explanation will vary.)
9	B	**9**	repair		
10	A	**10**	The <u>tiger was a bolt of lightning</u> as it went after its prey.		

Lesson #13		Lesson #14	Lesson #15
1	had (pedaled) had (learned)	**1** Mom will drive <u>me</u> to softball practice.	**1** foxes latches brushes
2	was looking	**2** Your chores are to make your bed, take out the trash, and set the table.	**2** will be shopping
3	A B	**3** (lovely) <u>green</u> (strange) <u>yellow</u>	**3** ✓ Mom says I <u>can</u> stay after school for play practice.
4	(under) the bed (inside) the house	**4** (shoes) that	**4** (on) the table (in) the cooler
5	The girls went to the mall, <u>and</u> they met friends at the movies on Saturday.	**5** <u>hospital</u> (where)	**5** here
6	two	**6** (Wood)^sp you like to come to my house for (diner)^sp? Would you like to come to my house for dinner?	**6** disrespected
7	April Tues. Monday Dec. Aug. Sun.	**7** I already have my bathing suit, but Jackie thinks I should bring a towel and sunscreen, too.	**7** The <u>driver was boiling mad</u>.
8	teeth scarves selves	**8** B	**8** (a) (cricket) (times) (square)
9	✓ Everyone came on time, but Juliet had to leave early.	**9** Example: | Cause	Effect
---	---
I stepped on a nest.	I got stung by a wasp.
I overslept.	I was late for school.		**9** C
10	B	**10** (Answers will vary.)	**10** I have the cutest dogs in the world. Their names are Madison and Wilson.

Lesson #16		Lesson #17		Lesson #18	
1	his their	**1**	its her their	**1**	verb, adjective, or adverb
2	when	**2**	<u>is painting</u> present	**2**	<u>Mrs. Pulaski</u> (her) <u>pizza</u> (it) <u>notes</u> (them)
3	✓ declarative	**3**	Richard is good at basketball, but Mary thinks volleyball is her best sport.	**3**	when
4	with	**4**	<u>during the storm</u> during	**4**	Mark horse
5	their	**5**	objects in space	**5**	(noisy) <u>younger</u> (shiny) <u>new</u>
6	Mark said, "I think I broke my arm!"	**6**	<u>can get</u> willingness <u>can hurt</u> possibility	**6**	"What time will you be home from work?" asked Jeanne.
7	peaches wolves children	**7**	(We) <u>read</u>	**7**	parties libraries skies
8	(dim) <u>rectangular</u>	**8**	B	**8**	skimpy
9	building	**9**	<u>jeremy</u> and <u>i</u> borrowed the book <u>*hatchet*</u> from <u>mrs</u>. <u>ross</u>.	**9**	unbuttoned rewrite
10	uneducated illiterate	**10**	look	**10**	~~Competitions too.~~ Example: She performs in competitions too. (Sentence will vary.)

Lesson #19		Lesson #20		Lesson #21	
1	were torn	**1**	will come will run	**1**	driven written
2	I want to buy a new video game, (so) I am saving my money. Jason wanted to go on the trip, (but) he missed the bus.	**2**	men's children's	**2**	will be arriving future
3	will be bringing future	**3**	where	**3**	B A
4	They left the ¢over off of the pool ⊙ sp Did you (no) that tonight there will be ⋏ full moon? a	**4**	large (round) small (oval)	**4**	for near
5	They left the cover off of the pool. Did you know that tonight there will be a full moon?	**5**	We tied up the boat at the dock. We saw a big storm was coming.	**5**	Casey will visit aunt sarah next Weekend.
6	from her friend from	**6**	We went to the shedd aquarium last (Saterday). sp	**6**	"Are we going camping this weekend?" asked Monique.
7	Dora put on her helmet, and she rode her bike to school.	**7**	Shaundra got an A on her test, so her mother made a special dinner.	**7**	Andrew Jackson was very poor as a child, and he became President of the United States. (**or** but, yet) (Answers will vary.)
8	drowsy	**8**	F I	**8** — **10**	Example: wink picture bear (Answers will vary.)
9	The school was closed because there was no electricity.	**9**	hair		
10	earlier	**10**	C		

Lesson #22		Lesson #23		Lesson #24	
1	I me	**1**	Monroe ... himself Clay and I ... ourselves	**1**	warmest colder
2	~~Nicoles'~~ Nicole's	**2**	its	**2**	where
3	when	**3**	is performing	**3**	B A
4	new purple old brown	**4**	between	**4**	tiny young giant old
5	not equal	**5**	too	**5**	The cat's real name is lady harrington.
6	miss grey read us the book charlotte's web.	**6**	The teacher shouted, "It's time to come inside!"	**6**	I like carrots, but golden beets are my favorite.
7	jogging shipping	**7**	I want to ride that roller coaster, but I'm not tall enough.	**7**	F F I I
8	informal English formal English	**8** — **10**	Example: 	Cause	Effect
---	---
It was raining.	Mary took an umbrella to work.
The furnace stopped.	The kitchen was very cold.
The puppy was left alone too long.	She had an accident on the rug.
The teacher wasn't feeling well.	She went home at noon.	 (Answers will vary.)	**8**	S A
9	S A			**9**	Henry was lost, and he didn't know how to find his way home.
10	We are making cookies. Would you like to help?			**10**	mis- pre- dis- re-

	Lesson #25		Lesson #26		Lesson #27
1	will grow	**1**	earlier higher	**1**	fastest most beautiful
2	Shauna watered the flowers, cut the grass, and trimmed the shrubs.	**2**	birds' girls'	**2**	were eating
3	~~Twice as large as Texas.~~ Example: It is twice as large as Texas. (Sentence will vary.)	**3**	when	**3**	possibility of something
4	<u>curved</u> (brown) <u>triangular</u> (black)	**4**	sixteen warm	**4**	among
5	was playing	**5**	~~And many animals too.~~ Example: Many animals live there too. (Sentence will vary.)	**5**	~~With sharp claws.~~ Example: They have sharp claws. (Sentence will vary.)
6	Our Giants Jackson Park Sunday	**6**	Barbara asked, "Has anyone seen my slippers?"	**6**	The coach instructed, "Run as fast as you can to first base!"
7	cuter cutest	**7**	<u>Allison</u> <u>turned in her social studies report</u>.	**7**	Regina|brought a plate of brownies to her neighbor.
8	snow clouds	**8**	Example: Want to come over for dinner? Lemme check but I'd love to! (Answers will vary.)	**8**	A
9	Example: <table><tr><td>Cause</td><td>Effect</td></tr><tr><td>The road was closed.</td><td>We took another route.</td></tr><tr><td>The door was locked.</td><td>I had to wait outside in the rain.</td></tr></table>	**9**	antonyms	**9**	perturbed: A, D serene: B, C
10	(Answers will vary.)	**10**	cause	**10**	bendable

Lesson #28		Lesson #29		Lesson #30	
1	did fell shook	1	blue large pungent homemade dark windowless	1	Example: Brandon <u>thoroughly</u> washed the car. (Adverb will vary.)
2	when	2	where	2	is planting
3	four yellow	3	are attending	3	two small square
4	(along) the beach (behind) the door	4	can could	4	(of) the mountains (between) his two friends
5	knew new	5	We are studying whales in science class. And also dolphins. science class is fun!	5	There their
6	This camping trip will be fun, but I hope no one gets poison ivy this year!	6	"What time does the pool open?" asked Monica.	6	D
7	hopeless	7	She is	7	Are you having a fun summer, or are you ready for school to start again?
8	impossible disagree	8	The little girl is crying because she lost her teddy bear.	8	before
9	antonyms	9	ordinary rare	9	umbrella roof
10	My I Main Street	10	B	10	Playful monkies climbed all over each other.